THE BIONIC WOMAN*

*A trade mark of, and licensed by,
Universal City Studios Inc.

PUBLISHED BY

BROWN WATSON

A HOWARD & WYNDHAM COMPANY

£1·25p

LINDSAY WAGNER

ALIAS
THE BIONIC WOMAN

the one time 'bit' actress that
now has a choice of parts

THERE CAN'T BE many major TV companies that would put themselves out on a limb (even if they are bionic) over a new series, backing it with vast sums of money and putting their faith in a comparative unknown actress. But that's what M.C.A. did when they decided to cast Lindsay Wagner in the role of Jaime Sommers, alias '*The Bionic Woman*'. It was a decision that sparked off a phenomenal success story, for not only did the series soar to chart-topping heights on both sides of the Atlantic, but it made Lindsay an 'overnight' star, and one of TV's hottest properties.

Up until '*The Bionic Woman*', Lindsay had been 'struggling' along as a 'bit' actress having appeared in TV series such as '*The F.B.I.*'; '*Owen Marshall, Counselor at Law*'; '*Night Gallery*'; '*Marcus Welby,*

M.D.' and *'The Rockford Files'*, as well as starring opposite Peter Fonda in the film *'Paper Chase'*. Then came her appearance as Steve Austin's girlfriend in *'The Six Million Dollar Man'*, when in a two-part story she was to prove that although Steve may be bionic, his heart was still in the right place, then be killed off in a fatal parachute accident.

But, for those two episodes, the show soared up to fourth place in the ratings and it was obvious to all concerned at Universal that, in the fair shape of Lindsay Wagner, they had a potential winner and their faith was justified when the show became a real block-buster.

Lindsay was born in Los Angeles on June 22 to Bill Wagner, a professional school photographer, and the former Marilyn Thrasher. At 13, she bagan dance studies with Jody Best, who shifted her from ballet to jazz and then to modern in the hope that her pupil would show some aptitude for one of them. But when the Pavlova within her failed to emerge, her mentor suggested that she study to be an actress and suggested her husband, James Best.

It was an excellent idea. Lindsay took to acting immediately, and with no two-left-feet problem, moved to the head of the class in short order to appear in a showcase production of Tennessee Williams' 'This Property is Condemned'. An MGM scout, impressed by her talent and quality, offered her the lead in a television series in which a teenage girl was the central character. Lindsay went for advice to Best, who took the position that she was not fully trained and that other chances would come her way. Not the least bit upset at missing out on a series, Lindsay became a sought-after photographic fashion model for Nina Blanchard.

After attending North Hollywood High School, she moved with her mother and step-father, David Douglas, to Portland, Oregon to finish her high school education. She was totally unprepared for Remona Reynolds, a drama teacher who had once been an actress herself, and who imparted all she knew to Lindsay in school plays which she directed, among them 'Stage Door' and 'Winterset'.

After graduating, Lindsay spent three months in France with a student group, then enrolled at the University of Oregon for a year, transferring for six months to Mt. Hood Community College in Portland. For a time, she studied singing and worked professionally with a rock group. Returning to Los Angeles in late 1968, she decided that acting was her forte. A number of people with unshakable belief in her as an actress urged her to get down to brass tacks and work professionally. Lindsay, who 'wanted to do it my way', held off until she felt emotionally ready.

Lindsay's talent caught the eye of Monique James, West Coast executive in charge of Universal's New Talent Development Program, and this led to a brief camera appearance in a 'Marcus Welby, M.D.' segment and to a contract in mid-1971. At first the roles were small but later became increasingly more challenging.

Lindsay met the challenge head on with amazing success and with her impressive background and rapidly ascending career, she is a 'star' in the true sense of the word.

Away from the TV screen, Lindsay lives with husband Allan Rider, director of Irving Music Inc. and the Almo Music Corp., in a rambling house set on an acre of land in Studio City, sharing space with two cats and a dog. Because of her hectic career, free time is very little, and she hasn't been able to discover any real hobbies. With the success of 'The Bionic Woman', Lindsay's future in TV and films seems secured for many years to come which can only be good news for all of us.

HIJACK!

T he big, yellow schoolbus laboured tiredly up
the twisting backroad, leaving Ventura air-
base many miles behind as it climbed slowly
into the hills. The engine growled as the driver
changed down into a lower gear, but Jaime Sommers could hardly hear it over the babble of excited
voices that filled the bus behind her. It was their first
natural history study trip in weeks, and the kids
were intent on enjoying themselves as much, and as
noisily, as possible. Jaime grinned, then turned and
sternly told them to quiet down. It didn't make any
difference.

The bus turned a corner and came out on to a
level stretch. The driver changed gear again, and
the rattling coach sped along the gently curving
road that took them round the hill. And then
suddenly the brakes were on. The bus shook with
the unaccustomed strain and ground to a halt.
Ahead of them, blocking the road entirely, were
two cars, each at a crazy angle.

"What's going on, Charlie?" Jaime asked the
driver, looking ahead to see two men walking
toward them, each carrying a long bundle wrapped
in canvas.

"Some kind of accident, by the look of things,
Miss Sommers," Charlie replied, opening the bus
doors as the men approached, waving.

Suddenly, and with blinding speed, the situation
changed. In an instant, the men had thrown off the
canvas wraps to reveal deadly automatic rifles, and
a second later they were on the bus. The first man
raced up the aisle past Jaime, the other prodded the
shocked driver with the barrel of his rifle. Behind
her Jaime could hear the kids screaming and
yelping in panic.

"Be quiet, be still and no one'll get hurt!" the
man at the front hissed. Through the windscreen,
Jaime could see two more men, also armed,
running toward them from the cars. She started to
get to her feet.

"Now hold on! What's going on here?" She
began, and suddenly something slammed heavily
into the back of her neck. She felt, for a moment, as
if the Empire State Building had fallen on her
head . . . and then she didn't feel anything any
more for a long time.

It was twilight when Jaime came round, and she realised she must have been out cold for five or six hours. She looked round, stunned. They were all still on the bus, and three of the older boys were gathered round her, on their knees. Further down the bus, she could hear the soft sound of weeping coming from a couple of the girls.

Sitting up and rubbing her neck and the back of her head gingerly with one hand, Jaime looked around. She had been laying in the aisle, where she had fallen, and now, with the boys' assistance, she climbed up into her seat and tried to gather her senses. The attack had just been too sudden, even for her to do anything about it.

"Sorry, kids . . ." she said after a moment, then looking back at the frightened, tear-stained faces of her class, suddenly realised they were in deep trouble. She tried to force a smile.

"Now listen, everything's going to be all right. We'll get out of this somehow. Now, Pete," she turned to one of the boys at her side, "I want you to tell me everything that's happened . . ."

She looked round toward the empty driver's seat. "Where's Charlie, for a start?"

"They left him behind, Miss," Pete began. "They told him to walk back to the base, and when he'd gone they said that ought to give them a couple of hours to bring us here and get us hidden. He's supposed to go to the base commander and tell him their demands . . ."

It all became clear to Jaime now. They'd been kidnapped, the whole busload of them, to be used as hostages by some group of fanatics. She realised they were in very great danger.

"And what were their demands, Pete?" she asked, trying to sound as casual as possible. Pete looked thoughtful, concentration creasing his young face as he tried to remember.

"I think . . . they wanted five million dollars for a start, and a light plane to be waiting for them at Ventura field tomorrow. It was to be loaded with . . . I'm not sure, but I think they said mortars, and two cases of bombs. They said all this had to be got together by noon tomorrow, otherwise . . ." his voice dropped to a whisper, "They said they'd kill all of us . . ."

One of the girls started to cry again. Jaime went over to her and put an arm round her shoulder, trying to comfort her, while turning back to Pete.

"How many of them are there? Do you know where we are?"

"There were four of them to start off with," Pete replied. "I think there's another one here, who wasn't in on the hold up. But they've all got automatic rifles, Miss. Some of them have got pistols, too, and I saw one with a couple of hand-grenades. I don't know where we are, though. Somewhere in the hills. It took an hour to get here, but I think the driver was going round in circles some of the time . . ."

Jaime nodded thoughtfully. Whoever these people were, they were taking no chances. She went over to the window and looked out, sizing up the situation. The bus had been parked under the overhanging branches of some trees, and there was brushwood stacked all along the side, covering the bus's yellow paint.

"They drew a green tarpaulin over the roof of the bus, too." Pete said, as if reading her thoughts. "I guess that's to disguise the bus from the air . . ."

She nodded. They seemed to be in a small box-canyon, well-shrouded with trees on all sides. It was an almost perfect hiding place. The canyon cut off sight from the ground, and the trees from the air. About twenty yards from the bus she could see a tumbledown old wooden shack, which she guessed was where most of the men were. One of them was pacing around outside, gun in hand. But why were they leaving them alone so much?

"There's no way out, Miss. The door's jammed . . . we tried it as soon as they left us alone, and they've somehow pulled the same trick on the emergency door. The only way we could get out is to smash a window, and they'd hear that straight away . . ."

She knew Pete was a bright boy, and he seemed to have got it all figured out. If he said the door wouldn't open, it wouldn't open . . . at least not to a normal person. But then Jaime was something more than that . . .

Sweeping back the hair from the right side of her face, Jaime listened carefully, scanning the area with her bionic ear. The footsteps of the man patrolling the canyon came in loud and clear, but there seemed to be no one else walking about. She turned her attention to the shack.

After a moment, she picked up two separate voices in conversation. That accounted for three of them, then. Straining to shut out all other sounds, she tried to locate the other two. Then she realised suddenly that at the very limit of her hearing, she was picking up the sound of soft snoring. At least one of them was asleep, and perhaps the other one was also. Perhaps . . . but it was a chance she would have to take. Quietly, she gathered her class around her.

"Now, listen," she whispered. "We're all going to be alright, but I can't do anything to help by staying here. I'm going to get out and go for help. Now, I don't want anyone to get frightened or doing anything stupid. When I've gone, Pete will be in charge. What I want you to do is wind down a window on the far side of the bus, and throw out some school books. When the guard goes round to see what's going on, I'll force the door and get out . . ."

"But, miss, the door's jammed tight. You'll never move it!"

Jaime smiled. "You just do your part, and leave the door to me. Now, when I'm gone, I want you all just to sit tight and don't do anything to upset them. No heroics. I'll be back as soon as I can . . ."

After a few protests and a little more explaining, Jaime got them to agree. As they moved to the back of the bus and wound down a window, Jaime went to the door and listened. There still seemed to be only one man moving about out there. She turned and signalled Pete.

The books hit the ground with a series of soft thuds, and almost immediately the man outside was running round the bus to see what was going on, gun in hand. Jaime was thankful that their captors had turned off the interior lights of the bus in order to hide it more thoroughly, for otherwise the guard would have been able to see easily what she was about to do.

Grabbing the handle of the folding doors in her right hand, she steadied herself and pulled inwards with ever-increasing strength. The door groaned, started to buckle, then, with a snap that sounded hideously loud to her, came open. She leaped out and raced off into the dark night, heading into the trees. From behind her came the sound of running footsteps, and then the sound of a rifle shot, closely followed by another.

As fast as her bionic legs would carry her, Jaime ran through the trees until she came to the foot of the canyon wall. There she paused, listening. Voices came to her ear: confused shouting, and then the slam of the shack door as it was wrenched open. Then there were footsteps, many footsteps, scattering out in all directions as the men began to search for her.

Looking up, Jaime saw that the canyon wall was sheer above her, about thirty feet high, with nothing in the way of hand or footholds to assist a climber. She smiled, tensed and leaped. Soaring upwards, she made the top of the canyon with ease, then turned, crouching, and listened and looked again.

The men were scattered throughout the canyon, searching for her . . . all of them except one who had stayed to guard the bus. Let them search then. They'd never think of looking for her up here. She sat down to wait until they had exhausted themselves. Then, when they had given up and settled down again, she'd be able to make her move.

Two hours passed by before they gave up. By then, the moon had risen, throwing a ghostly radiance on the canyon below, which showed that two men now stood guard on the bus instead of one. But the moon also cast deep shadows in places, and they would give her cover when she went into action. And now seemed to be the time .

Silently, Jaime launched herself over the edge of the cliff, dropping down into the canyon once more. Carefully, she crept through the trees, keeping to the shadows, and approached the bus again, noting the position of the two guards. One sat by the broken bus door, outside on the ground. The other prowled around near the edge of the trees. He would be the first to tackle then .

Without too much force, Jaime slapped her bionic right hand against the trunk of a tree, giving out just enough sound to attract the attention of the gunman without making him suspicious. He turned toward her, listening, and then sauntered slowly toward the trees. When she thought he was far enough from his companion, she let out a low moan.

"Don't shoot!" she called softly. "I think I've broken my leg! I'm over here . . ."

The man grasped his gun more firmly, then trotted forward toward the sound of her voice. But by the time he reached that spot, Jaime was no longer there, having leapt away into the trees.

"Over here . . ." she moaned, leading him on into the darkness. He came forward, slowed, then stopped, looking round. He seemed about to turn back and call to his companion, and Jaime knew that she had to strike right away.

Hurling herself through the air with a bionic-assisted spring, Jaime caught the man in the midriff, sending him tumbling on to his back. Before he could cry out, her right arm rose and fell heavily, chopping down on the side of his head. His body suddenly went limp, and he was still.

Moving away soundlessly, Jaime approached the bus. Everything seemed quiet. Most of the kids had fallen into a fitful sleep, and the guard by the door seemed relaxed and unworried. Noting his position carefully, Jaime moved toward the bus from the opposite side. Where the man was sitting, there was no way Jaime could approach him without being recognised, except from the back. And his back was against the bus.

The leap had to be judged to a nicety, not only to land exactly on target, but to get under the tree-branches which hung over the top of the bus, a few feet above. Jaime knew she only had one chance to

get it right. With a shrug, she took it, and leaped . . .

Twigs brushed her hair as she soared over the bus, and then she was coming down fast, feet first. She crunched into the shoulders of the sitting man with stunning force and he keeled over, silent, limp as a sack of potatoes.

Looking round, she saw Pete looking at her wide-eyed. She raised a finger to her lips, then moved to the door and stuck her head inside the bus.

"Get everyone down on the floor," she whispered. "You get into the driver's seat. I'm going across to the shack. When I raise my hand, you hit the horn hard . . . and then get down on the floor as well. Got that?"

Pete nodded, though he obviously didn't know what was going on. Quietly he moved back into the bus, and started to get his friends down out of sight. Jaime grabbed a rope attached to the tarpaulin and gently dragged it off the roof of the bus.

The tarpaulin was big. Ten or twelve feet wide and about thirty feet long. And it was very heavy. But to the Bionic Woman it was no difficult task to drag it across the canyon toward the shack. Carefully, she spread the 'back' end across in front of the shack, dumped down the rest of the tarpaulin, and took a firm hold on the 'front' with her right hand. Her left hand she raised, and waved. Pete gave the horn a ferocious blast.

Placing both hands on the tarpaulin, Jaime looked over her shoulder toward the shack, only a few feet behind her. The door suddenly swung open, and the three remaining men rushed out, guns in hand. They had barely enough time to see Jaime, to hesitate and try to stop their headlong run, before she was leaping up into the air, over their heads, toward the shack roof. Just before she landed, she released the tarpaulin. It fell over the three men like a huge tent, and collapsed down on top of them.

After that, it was the work of a moment for Jaime to leap down to the ground again and aim a series of savage blows at the three struggling forms trapped in the folds of the tarpaulin. And a second later, it was all over. Dusting off her hands, Jaime walked back to the bus, whistling.

"Make sure they're tied up good and tight, Pete," Jaime told him, after she had loaded the five men on to the bus. The kids, now relieved and happy, went to work with a will. "Oh, and if they wake up before we get back to the base, you might point a gun at them," she added. "But for heaven's sake don't pull the trigger!"

"Miss Sommers, I want to ask you something," Pete said as Jaime climbed into the driver's seat. "How did you do that? Overcome five men with guns?"

"Don't worry about it, Pete. All you need to know is that I'm going to get you back to the base safe and sound . . ." She smiled. "Besides, I'm your teacher, aren't I? I'm supposed to be able to look after you . . . to know how to do *everything*."

"Now, I wonder how you start this thing . . .!"

ANYTHING YOU CAN DO...

What would you do if you wanted to change a flat tyre and you didn't have a jack handy? Well if you were the Bionic Woman, all you'd have to do is use your Bionic arm to pick up the car. At least that's what she looks like she's doing and pretty well, too, when you consider that it takes three hefty fellahs to do the same thing. Of course we all know there's a trick to it. How's it done? Turn to page 57 and find out.

BIONICS –
yesterday's dreams...
tomorrow's realities

THE BIONIC WOMAN is the hit programme of the day, one of the most successful science fiction programmes ever brought to the television screen. But is it all *fiction*? The anser's 'No'... there's quite a lot of solid science fact in the stories as well. So let's take a look at some of the aspects of Bionics, both in fact and fiction...

'Bionics' is a fairly new word, being a contraction of *Bio*logical Elect*ronics,* and that more or less sums up what the new science is about. It comes in two parts: surgical replacement and the construction of artificial body parts . . . and in these days of transistors and printed circuits that takes it into the area of electronics.

Let's take a look at surgical replacement first, without the electronics. The first thing we find is that this has a surprisingly long history. False teeth, for instance, can be considered as replacement surgery, and these go back more than two thousand years! The Etruscans, who ruled Italy before the Roman Empire, carved false teeth from animal bones and attached them to the owner's natural teeth with gold wire. And George Washington, the first president of the United States had a very uncomfortable set of false teeth carved from Walrus ivory!

Limb replacement in historical times never reached such an advanced stage though. Probably the nearest our ancestors got to that was the wooden leg so often worn by pirates in Hollywood buccaneer pictures. But these weren't exactly noted for their movement . . . unless the pirate got woodworm in his peg-leg! Still, considerable progress was made with artificial limbs before we reached the age of miniaturised electronics. The artificial legs given to the famous World War 2 pilot Douglas Bader, while not 'working' like Jaime Sommers' bionic legs, did enable him to walk about and lead a fairly normal life.

If artificial replacement weren't working too well though, the obvious alternative was transplanting living organs from one body to another. This idea started up long before we had anything like the surgical skill to put it into effect, and Mary Shelley's novel, 'Frankenstein', which for so long has merely been considered as a good way of scaring ourselves silly, could turn out to be one of the great pieces of science-fiction prophecy. For the book was written in 1818, when anaesthetics were just something that doctors talked hopefully about and surgery was risky, to say the least. If you lost a leg, you were quite likely to lose your life as well . . . !

The story is well known: Dr Frankenstein collects various organs from recently deceased men, putting them together to make his 'creation' which he hopes will be the perfect man, and gives it life. The creation turns bad though . . . not because it has been given the brain of a criminal, as is usually shown in the films, but because of the inhumanity shown to it by the ordinary people it meets. The creation turns into a monster and, unkillable because its body is already 'dead', goes on the rampage, before being lost, eventually, in the icy wastes of the Arctic.

It was a remarkable story, especially considering that Mary Shelley was only nineteen years old when she wrote it, and the Frankenstein monster has become part of our modern mythology, especially as the story has been retold and continued countless times in films. Always though, the monster turns bad in the end and goes on the rampage, the moral being that there are some things, like the secret of life itself, that man shouldn't tamper with. In recent years, however, science has turned a great deal of its attention to just such secrets.

But is a 'monster' of the Frankenstein type possible? In the current state of medicine and sciences, the answer is no. But new developments are coming thick and fast in this field, and in the last twenty years or so enormous advances have been made in transplant surgery, the replacement of organs in an already living body.

The main problem with transplants is that the body tends to reject any living thing which is alien to it, such as somebody else's kidney. The body produces its own antibodies which attack any alien matter, and everybody produces their own personal antibodies. For many years, the only transplants that were possible were between identical twins, the only people whose bodies reacted in the same way. But recently doctors have managed to overcome this problem to some extent, and a large number of kidney transplants, the most common organs operated on, have been carried out. The more spectacular transplants, such as hearts and lungs, have not been so successful, though this is frequently because the patient is so weakened anyway that he dies, rather than from outright rejection of the new organ. The number of heart transplants has declined rapidly in the recent past.

With problems like this over transplants of single organs, it's easy to see why we're still a long way from building a Frankenstein type monster, even if the problem of bringing it back to life could be

solved. But where rejection doesn't enter into it, we have the technology to perform massive operations. In China a few years ago, a girl was hit by a train. Her left foot was crushed, as was her right leg between the thigh and ankle. Rather than give her *two* artificial legs, they gave her one . . . and transplanted the right foot onto her left leg! Having got used to the strangeness of the idea, the girl is walking around fairly normally . . .

But let's turn away from these grisly matters, and get back to the engineering side. How many people do you know who wear hearing aids? Well, that's how many bionic people you know! A hearing aid is an electronic device which amplifies sound, transmitting it through into the ear where the nerves convert it into electrical impulses which are carried to the brain. Jaime Sommers' Bionic Ear just takes this one step further . . . it's a sort of super hearing aid, which is actually implanted in her ear, rather than worn on the outside . . .

The Bionic Arm is also with us, though not in such an advanced form as that seen on the television screen. As far back as the late 1960s American researchers had produced what was known as the 'Boston Arm', a replacement for a man who had lost his arm just above the elbow. Powered by a battery pack worn on the waist and enclosed in flesh-coloured fibre-glass, it took electrical impulses from the muscles in the upper arm which would normally do the work and amplified them to control the system of motors, chain-drives and jackscrews in the main body of the arm itself. The arm was provided with two hook-like claws, rather than a hand, with which the owner was able to perform a lot of normal everyday tasks, such as answering the telephone, and also was able to lift up to ten pounds in weight. But this is still a long way from the undetectable, fully mobile and artificially fleshed Bionic Arm of the television series.

As far as lifting great weights is concerned, some progress has been made on that score as well. An invention known as a 'powered exoskeleton' fits round a normal human body, with electrically controlled metal arms and legs which are moved by the operator, and which move with him. Its huge claw-like hands can be used to lift weights of up to 1500 pounds. With new advances in miniaturisation, it may not be long before its possible to put such weight-lifting capabilities into a real Bionic arm.

What can be done with arms can also be done with legs of course, though legs which can leap, or move any faster than a slow walking pace seem a very long way off, if only because we've not yet discovered any way of making mechanical motors and levers react anywhere near as quickly as the almost perfect machine that is the human body.

So, as we can see, *The Bionic Woman* is a long way from being 'just science fiction'. It takes what we know today, and what we've already achieved, one or two steps further. But let's look even further ahead, into the distant future, and see what this line of research could provide for us . . .

The most obvious, and a well-loved subject among science-fiction writers, is the completely non-human robot. And once again, this is an idea that's been around for a very long time indeed.

Legends which grew up after the death of the famous Roman poet Virgil, who lived in the first century B.C., made him out to be a sorcerer, and one of his accomplishments was said to be the building of bronze men which moved with a life of their own. According to Chinese historical records, a statesman called Chuko Liang built 'wooden oxen', around 230 A.D., which also moved under their own power, and carried his army's supplies. He even left a written description of them, which survives to this day . . . but unfortunately no one can make any sense of it!

We have robots today, of course, machines which move under their own power and perform simple tasks, but these are all controlled by people, even if they are a great distance away. The usual idea of a robot is that it should have its own computer-brain, and be able to make decisions for itself. And it does seem likely that before too many years have gone by, we will be able to build machines that can think for themselves, in a limited fashion at least. We already have machines which have learned to 'feel' emotions, reacting to things with anger, fear or attraction, and other computers capable of taking decisions sufficiently well to play chess and win. And if our knowledge of miniaturisation, artificial limbs and computers continues to

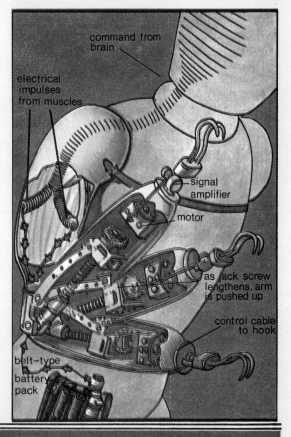

command from brain

electrical impulses from muscles

signal amplifier

motor

as jack screw lengthens, arm is pushed up

control cable to hook

belt-type battery pack

advance at the same rate as it does today, a human-shaped thinking robot is a very real possibility.

The ultimate form of robot is the android, a robot so perfectly constructed and covered in artificial flesh that it is indistinguishable from an ordinary human; and these too have been turning up in science-fiction television shows and films. A similarly far-out concept is the Cyborg, short for *Cyb*ernetic (computerised) *Org*anism, the ultimate idea in Bionic men . . . a human brain inside a body which is entirely mechanical and computerised.

And finally, we have genetic engineering, a concept which might be described as a merger between robotics and the Frankenstein idea. It looks as if it might be possible to alter the make up of a person by altering the genes in his cells before he is born, so he grows up differently . . . with gills, perhaps, for working and breathing underwater, or with superdeveloped muscles. The subject is still very controversial, dealing as it does with the secrets of life itself, and most religions find it highly offensive. But it looks possible, and if we do ever have a Dr Frankenstein in the future, it seems likely that this is the field he'll be working in. Could we really have someone resembling the fictional Doc Savage, the 'Man of Bronze'? Or even a comicbook Superman? We'll just have to wait and see . . .

In the meantime, we have Jaime Sommers, the Bionic Woman, and her adventures to enjoy. And if she's not as realistic as a powered exoskeleton, or as mind-stretching as a Cyborg, one thing's for sure . . . she's certainly a lot prettier!

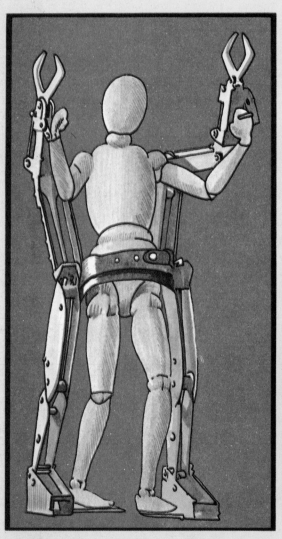

An artist's impression of a powered exoskeleton.

Frankenstein's 'Creation' – early Bionics?

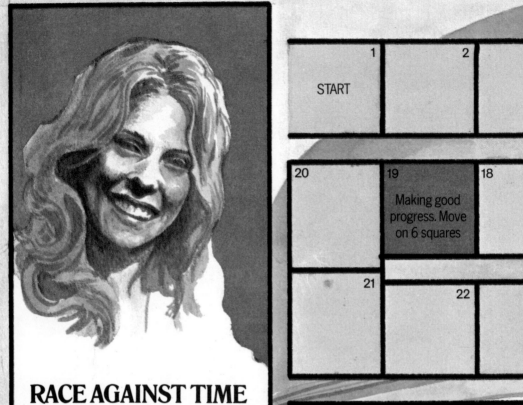

START 1	2	3
		Bion... yo...

20	19 Making good progress. Move on 6 squares	18	17
21		22	23 Lie... p...

RACE AGAINST TIME

A computer based in an advanced nuclear power station has had its tapes programmed for destruction. The explosion will cause total devastation. Those tapes must be removed and handed over for examination. There's only one person capable of taking on such a mission – THE BIONIC WOMAN. Join Jaime Sommers on this vital mission and see if you can overcome all the odds and help save the day. All you need to play the game is a dice and a counter per player. The first player to accomplish the mission is the winner.

34 Clear area in one throw. If not go back to 32	33 DANGER ZONE.	
35	36	

53	52	51 O.S.I. agent takes tapes. Move on to 58	50	49	48 Danger clear. Extra go	47
54 Transistor blows in leg. Progress slow. Miss a go	55	56	57 Meeting point with Oscar. Wait for him. Miss a go	58	59	

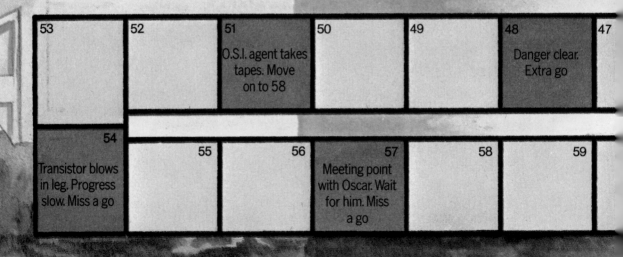

THE HEAVY MOB
A FILM SHOW AT O.S.I. HEADQUARTERS. BUT THIS ISN'T ENTERTAINMENT.
AND THE AUDIENCE NUMBERS ONLY TWO: OSCAR GOLDMAN AND JAIME SOMMERS, THE BIONIC WOMAN...
THIS IS THE FIRST OF THEM, JAIME... ELLIOT WHEELER. 5th GRADE BLACK BELT IN KARATE ... EX-PROFESSIONAL CHAMPION... A COUPLE OF MOVIE PARTS, BUT HE NEVER QUITE MADE IT.
SO HE PLAYS TO REMOTE SECURITY CAMERAS INSTEAD... AND PAYS HIMSELF FROM THE PROCEEDS!
THESE ARE THE OTHER TWO: HARVEY HENDRIX, ONE TIME HEAVYWEIGHT TITLE CHALLENGER... AND THE REFUGE FROM A CIRCUS IS KNOWN AS SANDOR THE STRONGMAN!
SILENTLY, THE FILM ROLLS ON, A RECORD OF ONE OF THE MOST DARING, AND MOST EXPENSIVE UNARMED ROBBERIES IN HISTORY...
YOU'RE KIDDING! NO ONE USES NAMES LIKE THAT ANYMORE!
IF YOU'D BROUGHT SOME POPCORN, OSCAR, IT WOULD HAVE BEEN A GREAT SHOW! BUT WHAT'S IT GOT TO DO WITH ME?
ALL THOSE ROBBERIES INVOLVED THE SECURE TRUCKING CO., JAIME. SOMEONE ON THE INSIDE'S GIVING INFORMATION TO THE CROOKS.
YOU'RE GOING IN AS SECRETARY TO LAZENBY, THE BOSS. HE'S THE ONLY ONE WHO'LL KNOW WHO YOU ARE. SOMEHOW YOU'VE GOT TO FIND OUT WHO'S TIPPING THEM OFF.

THE BIONIC WOMAN QUIZ

Here it is – a super 'Bionic' quiz for you to enjoy. All the answers to the fourteen questions set can be found in this book. See how many you can get right

1 What is the TV name of the Bionic Woman?
2 What is her profession?
3 Who is the person that sends her on her assignments?
4 Which organisation is he head of?
5 Where was Lindsay Wagner born?
6 What is her birth-date?
7 Which two words go to make up 'Bionic'?
8 What running speeds can the Bionic Woman reach?
9 Which parts of the Bionic Woman are actually Bionic?
10 Lindsay once appeared in the play 'This Property is Condemned'. Who wrote it?
11 Lindsay has some pets. What are they?

12 What tragic accident led to the operation that made her Bionic?
13 At the time of the accident, Jaime was dating someone. Who?
14 Which air-base does the Bionic Woman teach at?

RICHARD ANDERSON

ALIAS OSCAR GOLDMAN

ACTOR RICHARD ANDERSON believes he has established a TV first. Not only does he co-star simultaneously in two weekly MCA TV series, "The Bionic Woman" and "The Six Million Dollar Man", but he also plays the same character—Oscar Goldman of the OSI government agency in both series.

Although Richard was born in Long Branch, New Jersey, he spent the majority of his childhood in Los Angeles.

After serving as a war correspondent for the Army during World War II, he enrolled at the Actors Lab in West Hollywood and further perfected his craft at the Lobery Theatre in Santa Barbara and the Laguna Playhouse in Laguna Beach.

Spotted by a talent scout from MGM he was signed to a contract at the most prestigious studio of that time.

Anderson broke the highly-prized contract to appear in Stanley Kubrick's acclaimed "Paths of Glory", followed by "The Long Hot Summer" and "Compulsion". A Theatre Guild offer followed and he left Hollywood briefly for the lead in "The Highest Tree" on Broadway.

Returning to Hollywood, Anderson ventured into television by doing guest spots and regular roles on series such as "Bus Stop", "Perry Mason", "Twelve O'Clock High", "Big Valley", "Mannix", "Mod Squad" and "Ironside" for MCA TV. He took time out from television to co-star in "Tora! Tora! Tora!", an assignment he particularly enjoyed since it paved the way for three more features: "Along Came a Spider", "Macho Callahan" and "Doctor's Wives".

After a stint in another television series, "Dan August", Anderson worked on two more films: "The Honkers" and "Play It As It Lays" for Universal.

Richard is a Beverly Hills resident who devotes his energies to tennis, bike riding and photography. Recently he has taken up cross-country skiing.

VITAL STATISTICS
Birthplace: Long Branch, New Jersey
Birthdate: August 8
Height: 6ft. 3in.
Weight: 175lbs.
Hair: Brown
Eyes: Brown

Help Jaime find her way through the maze and back to base

THE BIG PAYOFF

"It's dangerous. Don't have any illusions about that . . . but you're the only agent I can send. You look enough like Cathy Russell to get away with it; and you do have the capabilities to get out of a jam. We'll be close by if you need us . . ."

Jaime Sommers remembered Oscar Goldman's words as she steered the car slowly along the narrow, winding road through the hills just south of the Mexican border. A few miles ahead lay the small, out-of-the-way border checkpoint, and there, she knew, her first problem would lie. She wondered how the real Cathy Russell would have handled things. But when the agents from the Office of Scientific Investigation had caught the woman, she hadn't yet thought of how she was going to smuggle half a million dollars across the border, so she couldn't tell them anything. But she had talked about virtually everything else. The offer of immunity from jail . . . a Mexican jail at that . . . had loosened her tongue considerably.

At a roadside eating house about two miles inside the American border, she was to meet her contact man. Then she had to persuade him to take her back to the leader of the organisation. After that, she was on her own. Although come to think of it, she was pretty much on her own right now. When she had asked Oscar what would happen if she got caught at the border post, his instructions hadn't run to the usual "Don't worry, we'll get you out somehow . . ." All he said was "Don't get caught . . ."

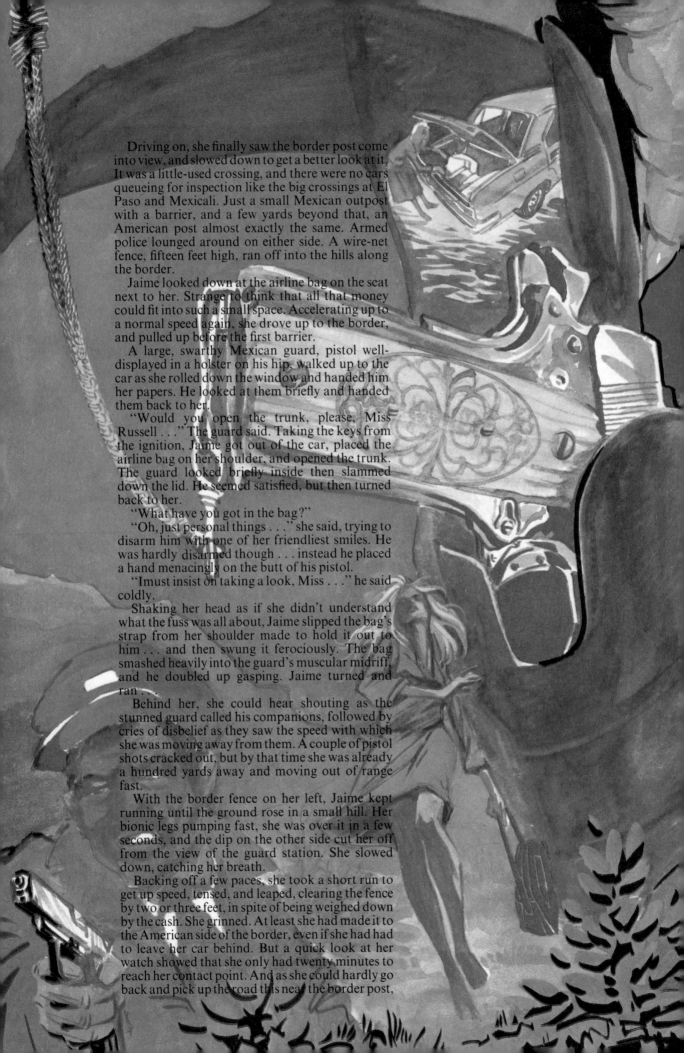

Driving on, she finally saw the border post come into view, and slowed down to get a better look at it. It was a little-used crossing, and there were no cars queueing for inspection like the big crossings at El Paso and Mexicali. Just a small Mexican outpost with a barrier, and a few yards beyond that, an American post almost exactly the same. Armed police lounged around on either side. A wire-net fence, fifteen feet high, ran off into the hills along the border.

Jaime looked down at the airline bag on the seat next to her. Strange to think that all that money could fit into such a small space. Accelerating up to a normal speed again, she drove up to the border, and pulled up before the first barrier.

A large, swarthy Mexican guard, pistol well-displayed in a holster on his hip, walked up to the car as she rolled down the window and handed him her papers. He looked at them briefly and handed them back to her.

"Would you open the trunk, please, Miss Russell . . ." The guard said. Taking the keys from the ignition, Jaime got out of the car, placed the airline bag on her shoulder, and opened the trunk. The guard looked briefly inside then slammed down the lid. He seemed satisfied, but then turned back to her.

"What have you got in the bag?"

"Oh, just personal things . . ." she said, trying to disarm him with one of her friendliest smiles. He was hardly disarmed though . . . instead he placed a hand menacingly on the butt of his pistol.

"I must insist on taking a look, Miss . . ." he said coldly.

Shaking her head as if she didn't understand what the fuss was all about, Jaime slipped the bag's strap from her shoulder made to hold it out to him . . . and then swung it ferociously. The bag smashed heavily into the guard's muscular midriff, and he doubled up gasping. Jaime turned and ran . . .

Behind her, she could hear shouting as the stunned guard called his companions, followed by cries of disbelief as they saw the speed with which she was moving away from them. A couple of pistol shots cracked out, but by that time she was already a hundred yards away and moving out of range fast.

With the border fence on her left, Jaime kept running until the ground rose in a small hill. Her bionic legs pumping fast, she was over it in a few seconds, and the dip on the other side cut her off from the view of the guard station. She slowed down, catching her breath.

Backing off a few paces, she took a short run to get up speed, tensed, and leaped, clearing the fence by two or three feet, in spite of being weighed down by the cash. She grinned. At least she had made it to the American side of the border, even if she had had to leave her car behind. But a quick look at her watch showed that she only had twenty minutes to reach her contact point. And as she could hardly go back and pick up the road this near the border post,

it was going to have to be run across rough country. Transferring the shoulder bag to her right arm, where her bionic hand could get a better grip, she set off up the nearest hill at an easy, thirty mile per hour jog-trot.

Eighteen minutes had passed when Jaime arrived at the Hard Road Cafe, a greasy diner that served mainly long-distance truck-drivers. Fortunately though, she didn't have to go inside. Following instructions, she sat herself on a fence at the edge of the car-park and waited. A few minutes later, a large black convertible pulled up next to her.

"Hand it over, Lady" the driver commanded. Jaime shook her head.

"No way . . . I got new instructions . . . I'm to see this through to the end. Besides, I had a little trouble with my car . . . you wouldn't leave a lady stranded, would you?"

The man looked at her strangely for a moment. Obviously he had not expected this, and didn't know what decision to take. While he hesitated, Jaime hopped off the fence, opened the rear door of the car and got in. The man looked at her once, shrugged, and turned the car out on to the road. Soon they were cruising northwards at an even fifty. Jaime smiled slightly, breathing an inward sigh of relief. So far so good.

Half an hour later, the car turned into the driveway of a large house on the outskirts of a small town. Both Jaime and the driver got out and headed toward the front door.

"Wait here . . ." the man said, entering. A few moments later he was back, signalling Jaime to follow him. He led her through the house to a large room at the back of the building, fitted out as an office. A middle-aged man with blond, greying hair, who introduced himself as Bedford, told her to sit down. The driver went out silently.

"You shouldn't be here, Miss Russell," Bedford began sternly. "You had your instructions. The money was to be handed over to my driver."

Jaime shrugged. "Instructions change."

Hoisting the airline bag on to her lap, she opened it, placed it on the desk and pushed it toward him.

"There's our part of the bargain . . ." she said.

Bedford picked up the bag and looked inside. Bedford nodded, satisfied, and shut it. "I shall have to have it checked, of course, before we fulfil our part . . . but it shouldn't take long . . ."

Bedford got to his feet, taking the bag, and walked across the room to a wall of bookshelves. Taking a key from his pocket, he opened up a panel, carefully disguised as the spines of a set of business manuals, and stepped close. Jaime could hear the tumblers clicking on a wall safe, hidden behind the panel. Bedford placed the bag inside, closed it up, and turned back to her.

"Now, as for handing the guidance-system plans to you . . . it's not that I don't trust you, of course, but if you're going to take them back instead of Leski, I'm going to have to check this out with Galindez."

"Be my guest." Jaime replied, confident in the knowledge that Galindez was one of the people the O.S.I. had picked up at the same time as they had made their original swoop to get the real Cathy Russell. Bedford picked up the phone and dialled.

Using her bionic ear, Jaime listened in to the faint voice from the other end of the line, and winced. To her, Oscar's voice was instantly recognisable, and his fake Mexican accent was so bad that she was sure Bedford would realise what was going on. But he obviously had never spoken directly to the real Galindez.

"Here, speak to him . . ." Bedford said suddenly, thrusting the phone toward her.

"Hello, Mister . . . uh . . . Galindez. Yes, everything's going all right. No, there's nothing to worry about . . ." She handed the phone back to Bedford.

"That's her . . ." She heard Oscar say at the other end of the line. "I'd recognise that voice anywhere."

Bedford seemed satisfied, ringing off, he smiled briefly.

"Okay, Miss Russell. We'll have the plans ready for you in the morning. I'll have one of my men show you to a room."

Jaime nodded, getting to her feet. A man came in, holding the door open for her. As she walked toward him, Bedford spoke again.

"By the way, a friend of yours is arriving here tomorrow . . . or perhaps more than a friend, I don't know . . . but I'm sure you'll want to stay round and meet him. Pete Stern . . ."

"How . . . uh . . . nice!" Jaime replied, and walked out rapidly.

In the room assigned to her, Jaime paced up and down, thinking furiously. If this man Stern was arriving tomorrow, the game would be all up, for he'd realise immediately that she wasn't the real Cathy Russell. And that meant that the original idea, where she got hold of the plans and got to safety before the O.S.I. agents moved in to clean up Bedford and his gang, would have to be scrapped.

Jaime decided there were two alternatives. The first was to get out of the house, contact the O.S.I., and have them move in. That way they would be sure of getting Bedford and his men, but there was also the possibility that the plans might be destroyed or hidden, and then maybe someone else would pick them up later. Besides, what if the O.S.I. men had lost track of her? She had no way of knowing that they'd be out there, or that there would be enough of them yet to mount a full-scale assault.

No, she would have to try to get the plans herself, tonight. They were the most important thing of all, and even if Bedford should be alerted by finding her missing in the morning, his escape wouldn't matter so much as them. And, she felt sure, the plans would be kept in the same wall-safe as the money.

At midnight, Jaime crossed to the door and silently tried the handle. It was locked. Outside the door, she could hear breathing. They'd set a guard

on her, so there was no point in breaking down the door. That would only give things away right at the beginning. She tip-toed quietly over to the window, and threw it open wide.

There was a thirty foot drop below, enough to deter any normal person from even thinking about escape. But for Jaime, it was simplicity itself. She sat on the window-sill, swung both legs out into the cold night air, and pushed herself off into space. Landing with perfect balance, she looked round quickly to see if the noise of her feet hitting the concrete patio had roused anyone's curiosity. Everything was perfectly silent. She ran off round the building toward the study.

The lock on the french door gave in with a quiet metallic groan under the pressure of her powerful right hand, and Jaime moved swiftly toward the bookshelves. With only the moonlight to guide her, it took a couple of minutes to find the false panel, but only a few seconds to think of how to get it open without the key. Inserting her fingernails into the crack round the edge of the panel, she found she had just enough leverage to pull it open sufficiently far to get a grip. With her right hand, she ripped the panel from it's hinges. And with her bionic ear hearing the falling of the tumblers in the safe's combination-lock like they were drum-beats, it didn't take long for that door to open either.

Inside the safe, she immediately found the airline bag . . . but nothing else. No plans, no papers, no microfilm. She turned away in disgust . . . and suddenly the lights went on.

"Is this what you were looking for, Miss Russell?" Bedford said, holding up a document file with Air Force and 'Secret' markings. On either side of him stood two men, each with a grim expression and a threatening pistol.

"Of course, I shouldn't really call you Miss Russell, should I?" Bedford continued, smiling and obviously enjoying himself. "You're certainly not the Cathy Russell I met in Berlin four years ago . . ."

"People change . . ." Jaime said simply, moving along the bookshelves slightly. The gun-barrels followed her every move. "What happens now?"

"We kill you, of course. Oh, I could have done it when you first got here, but I wanted a little time to check out your back-up forces first. There were two of your men keeping an eye on the place . . . and I use the word *were* advisedly."

Jaime's heart sank. There was no chance of outside help now.

"Do I get a last request?" she asked, forcing a smile.

"Perhaps . . . it depends what it is . . ."

"Well, I always say you can't beat a *good book!*" And, with the power of her bionic arm, Jaime swept the shelf clear of it's heavy reference books, sending them hurtling through the air toward the startled gunmen. One went down immediately, knocked cold by one of the books. The others ducked and dodged, trying to avoid the bruising volumes, their guns firing wildly. Bedford ducked back out of the

room as Jaime leapt forward swiftly.

By the time the three remaining gunmen had recovered enough to realise what was going on, Jaime was among them, striking out with blinding speed. Her right arm descended heavily on the head of one man. Her foot rose to kick another in the stomach, the powerful blow doubling him up. The third man she picked up bodily and hurled across the room to crash against the bulky desk. In seconds, it was all over, and there was only silence.

But Bedford was nowhere to be seen, and he still had the plans. She heard a door banging somewhere in the house, and set off in that direction. Arriving at the front entrance, she paused, listening carefully. There was no sound inside the house... the place was deserted but for herself and the four unconscious gunmen, but outside she could hear running footsteps. She listened carefully, and heard Bedford running back round the house. Smiling to herself, she walked back to the study.

Bedford came in from the patio a few moments later, running straight toward the open safe. It was quite empty.

"Is this what you were looking for, Mister Bedford?" Jaime asked from the other side of the room, holding up the half-million dollars. "You just couldn't bear to leave without it, could you?"

"Give me that!" he snarled, hurling himself toward her with a mad gleam in his eye. "You've ruined everything! But I'll have my money yet! Give it to me!"

So Jaime gave it to him..., in a swinging arc that smashed the bag into the side of his head with stunning force. Bedford flew gracefully through the air, and then landed in an untidy heap, knocked cold. Jaime plucked the plans from his hand and stood up.

Then, having put through a call to the number Oscar had given her to ring if she wanted help, she looked round at the five sleeping thugs scattered round the room. She stretched, yawning. It had been a long, tiring day.

When the O.S.I. agents arrived to clear things up, they found Jaime Sommers fast asleep as well...

PICTURES TO PAINT

THE scene is set, and outside a sound stage a red light flashes to warn everybody that the cameras are rolling. The script for this episode of 'Bionic Woman' calls for Jaime to *smash* her way out of a very solid cell somewhere deep inside a rambling, ancient castle. The cell walls are thick, made up from huge stone slabs. The door, studded and reinforced by metal cross-bands, is tough oak. All this we know from another scene, and what Jaime has just told her cellmate, a pretty, but nervous, computer operator.

"Stand back," Jaime says in a soft voice as she prepares for the action.

The director leans forward. So much depends on how the camera captures the door's destruction. The prop department has guaranteed the authenticity of the cell's *screen* appearance. Special effects have no worries—their skilled technicians have constructed many such doors since the series started.

Jaime moves across the cramped cell, leaps and executes a perfect drop-kick. Her feet slam against the door . . .

By the next morning the director has his 'rushes'— prints of the footage shot the previous evening. Most of the film will end up on the cutting-room floor, discarded as useless.

The projection machine grinds and flickering scenes flit across a silver screen. There is Jaime doing her bit for Oscar and country. As she lashes at the door with both feet the hinges give way, the supporting post tears agonizingly from the stone wall, and the massive door crashes outwards.

There is, as yet, no sound effects to accompany this action. Indeed, the scene as watched by the director is as phoney as all get out. It doesn't look like anything a television addict would believe for a single minute. The door pulling off its hinges and separating from the post shows shards of painted polystyrene flaking from the studded inner surface.

But, the director isn't worried!

Like everything Hollywood does, the fakery and trickery never reaches an audience's small screen. A few cuts, a masterly editing job splicing in frames from a second camera's footage—and what will be shown finally meets with egotistical approval by director and producer. Jaime has, once again, proved her bionic strength!

Some of the special effects used on shows like BIONIC WOMAN are stupendous. Most, though, fall into a category of commonplace routine. The door scene is normal for the technical crew. All it takes is imagination and the right camera angles to hide an accidental splitting of the plastic material used in the construction of supposedly indestructible doors, walls, metal bars.

When sound is finally added the end product will be highly acceptable. Believed by millions of avid series' watchers. Jaime's feet hitting the door, for example, will sound like a mule battering in anger on his stout stable walls. The grinding, complaining hinges ripping from their moorings will be a far cry from the soft plop heard in the studio 'take'. And the thunderous roar of the door meeting a stone floor will convince the onlookers that Jaime is

IS NOT BELIEVING

A cell door gives way under the impact of a Bionic drop-kick. But all is not as it appears.

Whether it be yanking an iron bar from a concrete frame (left), or appearing to tighten a nut at fantastic speed (right), you can bet that some form of camera trickery is at hand.

the world's most powerful woman.

To see Jaime perform her feats in normal speed would be a movie disaster. Let's face it, there is nothing quite so ordinary as grasping an iron bar and yanking it from a concrete foundation if it appears to be an everyday, matter of fact happening. The effect of power, strength, superhuman endurance comes across only because we *always* see bionics at work in dramatic slow-motion. Not the old-fashioned kind of slow-motion used by the early film-makers. But a kind of *speed* blurred urgency as perfected by expert cameramen of today.

When Jaime runs at incredible 60 mph cross-country record-breaking pace she is really doing a sedate 8 mph or thereabouts. Her every facial gesture and arm movement is exaggerated for the camera lens. The camera, however, is speeded up. The number of frames per second passing through the reels is being gauged to give the false impression

that superwoman Jaime can out-distance the flee-test animal on earth. This business of taking shots at high speeds and then playing tham back at a normal rate makes interesting viewing. What happens is that we 'see' the *complete* film going through the projection machine at the ordinary speed but those parts concerned with bionics have required more film footage than would normally have been the case.

The reverse procedure applies when we need to show Jaime, for example, unscrewing a nut holding an escape hatch when the scene calls for swift action to save our weekly heroine from certain death. The camera takes this shot at slower than normal speed with the result that we have Jaime's fingers working like greased lightning and the idea of fantastic ability is established again.

Movie trickery is an industry in itself. Hardly a single screen epic leaves the Hollywood 'dream factory' without being given an enormous helping

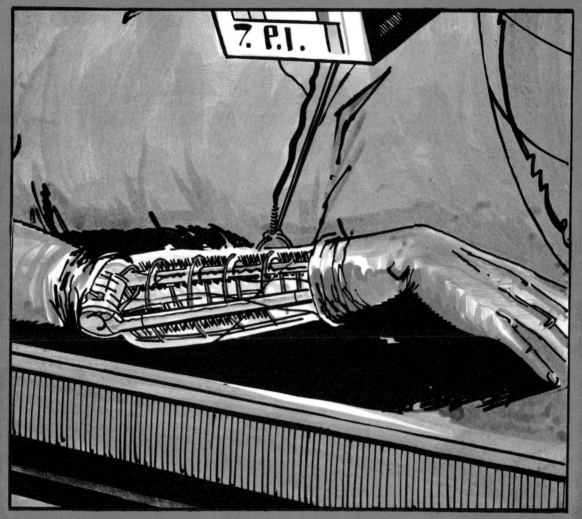

Major repair work is required on Jaime's arm and when the skin is pulled back the intricate wiring is revealed. To all intents and purposes it's Jaime's arm—or is it?

hand by the men and women of the special effects department. Think of Jaime once more. something has gone wrong with her bionic arm and adjustments are necessary. We see her on an operating table, her arm stretched out with its artificial skin layers drawn back to reveal those intricate wires where veins should be. On screen there is no way of telling that the arm does not belong to her. Study it carefully—it is attached to her shoulder the same as your arm is to your shoulder. The fingers move when she is asked to flex the bionic 'muscles'.

One way to show this is old hat. The sheet covering our delicious lady is 'arranged' to *fold* precisely where her real arm goes through a hole in the operating table and where the phoney bionic arm with its wires and transistors is left on 'show'. The fingers moving is a separate shot spliced into the finished film—a *stop action* insert.

Then, again, the scene could be fixed by a different type of trickery and the bionic arm wiring

a flexible plastic addition stuck on top of Jaime's genuine flesh so that the camera angle makes it look the right thickness for a woman's normal arm.

Each special effects department takes pride in doing its thing the fastest, easiest way possible. Costs are always important here. Too much cash spent on creating a monster, a futuristic city, a bionic feat and the whole series could be at risk. Budgets, these days, must be strict. Stars demand a high price for their 'services' and the various crews necessary to make a movie have to be paid an inflation-hit wage. In all adds up to cutting corners and no-one knows this more than the hard-pressed special effects man.

Seeing is believing is an old adage.

In movie-making, 'seeing is not believing' rules more than one roost. The camera never lies may have been a correct assumption years ago. Today, the camera never tells the truth. And, 'bionically speaking', that is genuine gen.

ANYTHING YOU CAN DO...

how it's done

How did Lindsay pick up the car? Well of course she didn't. The car is actually held up by a hydraulic jack attached to the lorry standing next to the Mini. By using the right camera angles it gives the impression that lovely Lindsay really does have super-human strength. Clever, isn't it?

BE CAREFUL, JAIME! REMEMBER, YOU COULD MEET *ANYTHING* UP THERE... FOREIGN AGENTS, BEARS.

MAYBE EVEN *LITTLE GREEN MEN IN A FLYING SAUCER?* DON'T WORRY, OSCAR... I'LL SEE YOU *TOMORROW.*

AND SO FASTER THAN ANY NORMAL HUMAN COULD MOVE, JAIME SOMMERS SETS OFF...

BUT SOON...

IT'D TAKE ME AGES TO *CLIMB* THIS... BUT THERE'S A *LEDGE* UP THERE...

...AND THERE'S NOTHING LIKE *ELEVATOR-LEGS* TO SAVE A *LITTLE* TIME...

AND YET THE JOURNEY STILL TAKES TWO HOURS. BUT FINALLY...

THERE SHE IS! NOW ALL I'VE GOT TO DO IS RIP OUT ITS *BRAINS...!*

THAT'S IT! VIRTUALLY INTACT, TOO!

BUT ENGROSSED WITH HER WORK, EVEN HER BIONIC EAR FAILS TO REGISTER A PRESENCE BEHIND HER. AND THEN...

WOK!

UUUUH!